A FRUIT IS BORN

STERLING NATURE SERIES

A
FRUIT
IS BORN

BY J. M. GUILCHER AND R. H. NOAILLES

STERLING PUBLISHING CO., Inc.   New York

STERLING NATURE SERIES

A Bird Is Born
A Butterfly Is Born
A Fruit Is Born
A Tree Is Born

OTHER NATURE BOOKS

Among the Rocks
Animal Travellers
101 Best Nature Games and Projects
The Deep Sea
Too Small to See
Treasures of the Earth
It's Snowing
Koala Bear's Walkabout
The Laughing Bird
Think, Mr. Platypus

Published in the United States of America
by Sterling Publishing Co., Inc.
419 Fourth Avenue, New York 16, N. Y.

Printed in France

1960

CONTENTS

The life of a flower is usually short. It blooms for a few days, sometimes for only a few hours, spreading out its stigmas (the parts that receive the pollen) and emptying its pollen-laden anthers (the parts that contain and develop the pollen). If the flower is lucky it will be fertilized by the fine dust (the pollen) brought to its female organ (the pistil) by gravity, wind or insects.

Then the flower fades. The stamens (the male fertilizing cells) wither and the colored petals fall to the ground. The fertilized pistil remains. There is nothing among the mass of leaves to show, at first glance, where the flower had been. Now the slow change begins as the pistil turns into a fruit and the ovules (immature seeds) become seeds.

All the plant's energy now goes into forming the seeds. The sap flows to the faded flower from the roots sunk deep in the soil and from leaves stretched out toward the light. It circulates in the wall of the ovary, it reaches the ovules, and the whole pistil begins to swell. In each ovule a tiny plant takes shape. This plantlet has a stem, a root, first leaves and tissues which store reserves of food. The walls of the ovule become thicker and harder, making a sturdy covering for the plantlet and its parts. When this development is completed the ovule will be a seed that can resist dampness, frost and dryness until it is able to germinate—sprout or begin to grow.

The pistil becomes a fruit enclosing the seeds. Often it forms the fruit by itself. Sometimes other parts of the flower help to form the fruit, but in every case the pistil plays the privileged role of seed container. We cannot understand the birth and structure of a fruit without first knowing the structure of the pistil from which it comes.

This structure takes very different forms in different species.

The pistil of the cherry blossom has an ovary, a style and a stigma.

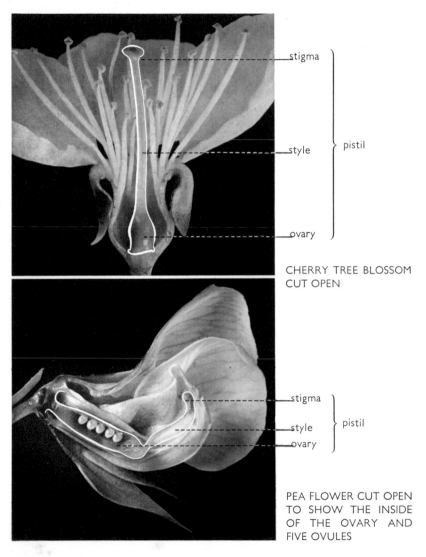

stigma

style ⎫ pistil

ovary

CHERRY TREE BLOSSOM
CUT OPEN

stigma

style ⎫ pistil

ovary

PEA FLOWER CUT OPEN
TO SHOW THE INSIDE
OF THE OVARY AND
FIVE OVULES

The pistil of the pea is made up of the same parts, but in different form.

The pistil of the hellebore, a poisonous herb, is made up of several

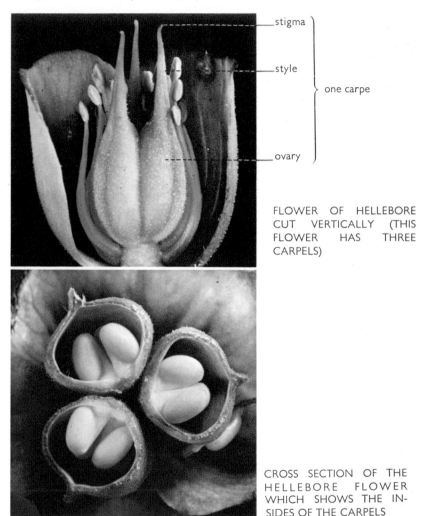

stigma ⎫
style ⎬ one carpe
ovary ⎭

FLOWER OF HELLEBORE CUT VERTICALLY (THIS FLOWER HAS THREE CARPELS)

CROSS SECTION OF THE HELLEBORE FLOWER WHICH SHOWS THE INSIDES OF THE CARPELS

adjoining parts. Each of these parts is called a carpel and together they form the pistil. Each carpel is made up of an ovary, a style and a stigma.

The hellebore has only a few carpels. Each contains many ovules. The anemone, on the other hand, has many carpels, each enclosing

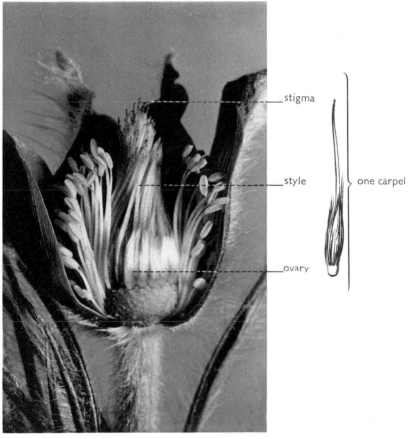

stigma

style

one carpel

ovary

ANEMONE FLOWER
(CUTAWAY VIEW)

a single ovule. The carpels are separate from each other but are packed closely together in a tuft-like formation.

The pistil of wild bryony, a plant of the gourd family, has three carpels.

three separate stigmas

three styles joined into one

the hollow interior of a carpel

three ovaries joined into one

FEMALE FLOWER OF BRYONY

At first sight these separate carpels look like only one. They cannot be separated; they are not merely next to each other—they are joined together. The three ovaries are also joined into one. This single ovary, in the form of a ball, is found below the flower. It must be cut across to show its division into three compartments. Each compartment is the hollow inside a carpel. The three styles are joined but the three stigmas are separate from each other. This is the only sign that there are really three carpels, not just one.

The pistil of the rose campion, a European herb, has five carpels.

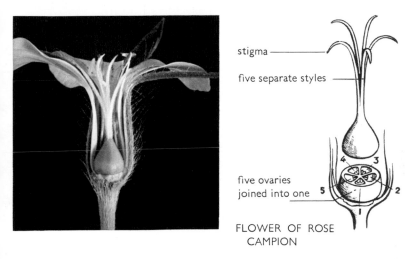

stigma ——————

five separate styles ——————

five ovaries
joined into one

FLOWER OF ROSE
CAMPION

The styles and the stigmas are separate; the five ovaries are united.
(The five inner partitions seen in the very young flower disappear
later, leaving an ovary consisting of one big chamber.)

two separate
stigmas

two styles
joined into one

two ovaries
joined into
one

wing

one carpel   one carpel

FLOWER OF MAPLE

The pistil of the maple is made up of two carpels. The ovaries and
the styles are united; only the stigmas are separate.

The pistil of honesty, another European plant, has two carpels joined together.

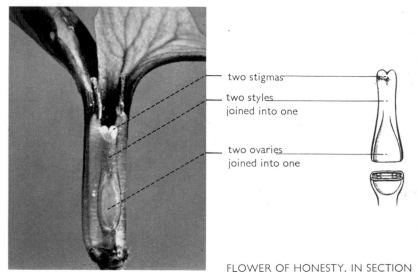

two stigmas

two styles
joined into one

two ovaries
joined into one

FLOWER OF HONESTY, IN SECTION

In the maple, rose campion and bryony, each carpel formed one closed cell.

In honesty, the arrangement is different. The wall of each carpel is not closed on itself; it does not make up a complete cell (Illus. 1). The two carpels are joined together side by side, making a common cell (Illus. 2).

A partition which develops later separates this common ovary into two compartments (Illus. 3). This partition is not made from the carpels. It is called a "false septum." (A septum is a wall that divides two cavities.)

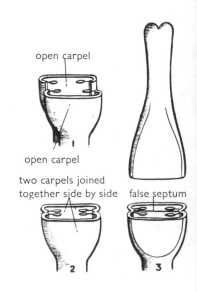

open carpel

open carpel

two carpels joined
together side by side

false septum

2

3

Once fertilized, the pistils develop in various ways.

In some species, the wall of the ovary becomes thick and fleshy. It forms one of two types of fleshy fruits. One type, containing stones or pits, is called a "drupe." Cherry, plum, apricot and peach are examples. The other type, containing pips or seeds, is known as a "berry." Here we have the grape, currant and tomato. We usually think of these juicy drupes and berries when we speak of fruit.

In other species, however, the ovary wall remains thin, while drying and hardening. This produces a dry fruit—chestnut, bean pod, poppy head, etc.

Both the soft and dry fruits serve the same purpose. They shelter the seed from damage and bad weather.

At last the moment comes when the seed is released. Fruits differ most in the way they scatter their seeds.

Sometimes the whole fruit drops from the branch. The berries and drupes rot on the ground, exposing their seeds and pits to the air. Acorns, beechnuts and hazelnuts (filberts) are strewn beneath the trees. Their dry shells continue to enclose the seed until it germinates. At that time the plantlet breaks through both the skin of the fruit and the seed wall. These dry fruits which do not open are called "achenes."

But many dry fruits do open when they are ripe and the single seeds break away from the mother plant. These fruits have various names according to the way they open and the number of carpels they have. A dry fruit consisting of a single carpel sometimes opens by splitting once down its length. It is then called a "follicle." Sometimes it splits lengthwise in two places to form two identical valves. It is then called a "pod." A dry fruit formed from united carpels is a "capsule." It can open by splitting, by a system of teeth, pores, valves, etc.

Each fruit tells its own story. Here are some examples chosen from common and not so common plants. First comes the story of the cherry.

DRUPES

A drupe is a fruit with a
fleshy outer part and a very
hard center which is the pit
that contains the seed.

(magnified 3 times)

How do cherry blossoms

(magnified 2 times)

turn into cherries?

(magnified 6 times)

1. CHERRY FLOWER CUT VERTICALLY
2 to 5. FIRST STAGES IN FORMATION OF
   THE FRUIT

THE CHERRY TREE

The pistil grows at the bottom of a cup formed by the base of the flower. The ovary has a very long style, ending in a stigma.

The fertilized flower fades. The ovary swells, splits the withered calyx (the green part between the petals and the stem) and becomes a little green cherry.

Within a few weeks the fruit will take on its characteristic size, shape and color.

The pistil forms the fruit. The ovary

swells; its walls become fleshy . . .

. . . while the pit forms around the seed:

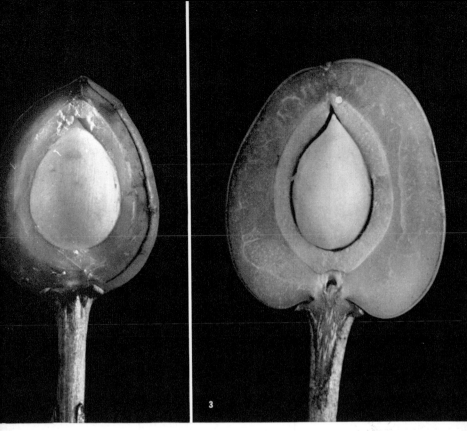

3

DEVELOPMENT OF THE OVULE AND THE WALL OF THE OVARY

The ovary (the bottom of Illus. 1) contains two ovules (only one can be seen in the photograph). One of these will not develop; the other, after growing much larger, will become the seed.

The wall of the ovary thickens and becomes sweet and fleshy. The inner part of the ovary becomes woody and forms a hard case (the nut) around the seed or kernel. This can be seen clearly in Illus. 3.

the ovary becomes a drupe.

The green walnut is the drupe of the walnut tree.

BERRIES

A berry is a soft fruit
containing seeds.

1. TIP OF A MALE BRYONY PLANT
2. TIP OF A FEMALE BRYONY PLANT
3 to 6. THE OPENING OF A FEMALE FLOWER AND THE DEVELOPMENT OF
THE FRUIT

BRYONY

Bryony is a climbing plant of the cucumber family, found growing mostly in hedges. It clings to its supports by tendrils coiled in spirals. Male and female flowers are found on separate plants. The female flower forms the fruit after it has been fertilized by pollen carried to it by insects. Its ovary becomes larger, while the sepals, petals and stigmas wither away.

The ovary of the bryony becomes a fleshy fruit . . .

1. FEMALE FLOWER
2. RIPE FRUITS
3. BRANCH BEARING FRUIT

Illus. 1 and 2 show the comparison between the ovules and the seeds. In Illus. 1 the wall of the ovary has been cut away to show the inside of one cell and the two ovules which it contains. In Illus. 2, one of the fruits has been cut across.

The ripe fruit is red. Its outer part is fleshy and the ovules have become large seeds with hard walls. The fruit is a berry; its pips are the seeds.

. . . whose skin encloses some seeds.

Each flower has formed a berry. (magnified 2 times)

Each grape is a berry developed from

1. BUNCH OF GRAPES
2. CLUSTER OF FLOWERS ON A VINE
3 to 4. PISTIL AND FRUIT CUT
    VERTICALLY

VINE FRUITS

The flowers of the vine are very small and greenish in color. Their corolla (petal formation) does not open out. It breaks off from the base of the flower and falls away to reveal a small pistil surrounded by six stamens. After fertilization, the ovary swells enormously. Its walls become sweet and fleshy throughout, forming the pulp of the grape. The pips are ovules which have become seeds.

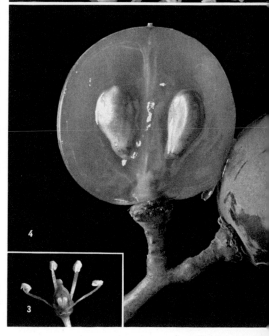

(magnified 4½ times)

(magnified 3 times)

one of the tiny flowers of the vine.

31

(magnified 3½ times)

Arum berries grow like the kernels on an ear of

(magnified 4 times)

corn. Currant berries grow in a loose bunch.

(magnified 5½ times)

Berries of the bittersweet are oval; those

(magnified 7 times)

of the black nightshade are perfect spheres.

(magnified 3 times)

Flowers and berries of the broom (a shrub of the

(magnified 6 times)

pea family) are carried on leaflike branches.

The berry of the catchfly or berry-bearing campion grows in the center of the calyx.

FOLLICLES

A follicle is a dry fruit
formed from a single carpel
which splits open from top
to bottom.

THE HELLEBORE

The poisonous hellebore spreads its modest little green flowers in the depths of winter.

Its pistil (Illus. 4 and 5) is concealed by the stamens (Illus. 3) which are, in turn, enclosed by the sepals and the petals. It is made up of several carpels next to each ·other. The number of carpels varies in different hellebore flowers; there are three in the flower shown here. Each carpel protects a double row of ovules.

After fertilization the carpels grow bigger and become fruits with dry skins which split open from top to bottom; these fruits are follicles. The ovules, which have become brown seeds, fall through the opening in the fruit.

The pictures on pages 42 and 43 show the development of the carpels and ovules.

5

(magnified 3½ times)

The hellebore has separate carpels.

Each carpel becomes a follicle.

The ovules turn into seeds which fall

When ripe it splits open.

through the opening in the fruit.

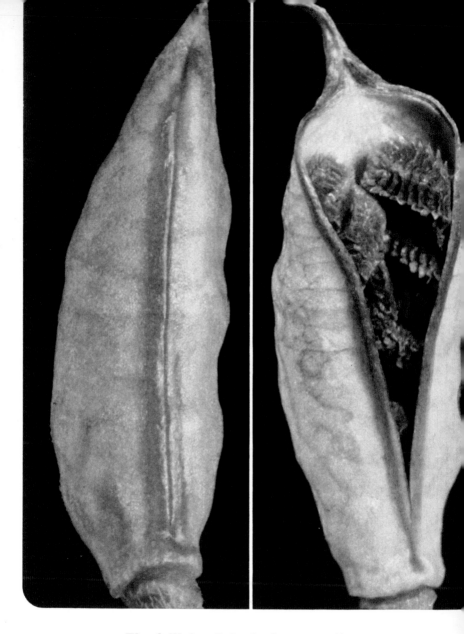

**The follicle of the larkspur splits
open from top to bottom.**

PODS

A pod is a dry fruit
developed from a single
carpel which splits open
from top to bottom in
two places, forming two
symmetrical valves.

THE PEA

The white corolla of the pea conceals a pistil (Illus. 3) whose shape already resembles that of the fruit (Illus. 2). This pistil consists of a single carpel containing several ovules (Illus. 4).

The pistil becomes a dry fruit and the ovules turn into seeds — small edible peas.

The ripe fruit splits open in two places, forming two valves and allowing the seeds to fall out.

The fruit is known as a pod.

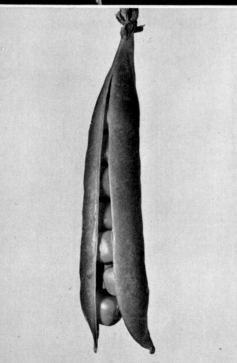

2

(magnified 2 times)

Like all other pods, the pea

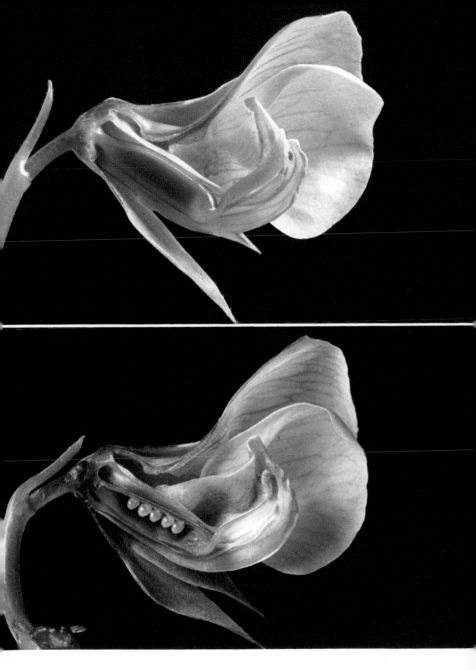

pod splits open in two places.

(magnified 6½ times)

The pod of the vetch is like the pea pod.

(magnified 22 times)

The pods of alfalfa are in spiral coils . . .

(magnified 10 times)

In these two species of alfalfa the pods are wound in a tight spiral.

. . . varying in appearance

(magnified 18 times)

This one is beginning to open: the top layer has already
split, revealing two seeds.

from species to species.

(magnified 3½ times)

The pod of the horseshoe vetch is an exception to the rule. It splits into several parts which do not open.

The horseshoe vetch is exceptional. Its

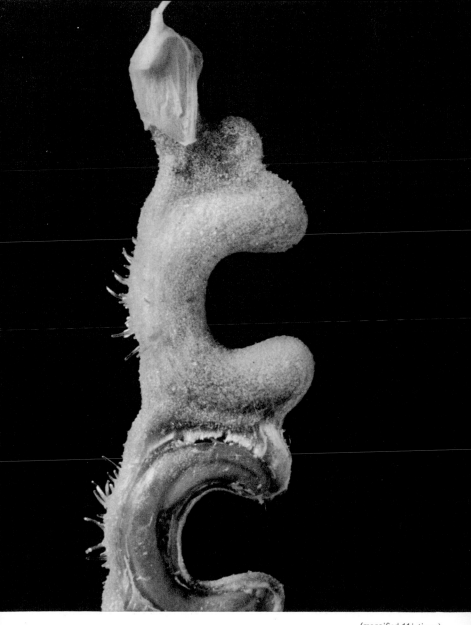

(magnified 11½ times)

The photograph shows one of these parts with the outer covering removed. It contains only one seed.

pod splits into crescent-shaped parts.

(magnified 2 times)

The empty pods of the lotus herb extend outward in all directions.

CAPSULES

A capsule is a dry fruit
formed by several united
carpels. The capsules of
different species open in
different ways.

(magnified 2½ times)
1. OPEN FLOWER OF ROSE CAMPION
2 and 3. INSIDE OF A FLOWER BUD

THE ROSE CAMPION

The Rose Campion is one of the most beautiful wild plants. The flower contains a pistil composed of five united carpels. The ovary (Illus. 2) contains many ovules (Illus. 3). Five styles grow from the top of the ovary. These may be seen more clearly in the photographs on the next few pages.

Pages 58 and 59 show the birth of the fruit. The top row of photographs shows, from left to right, the flower and its development after its petals have fallen.

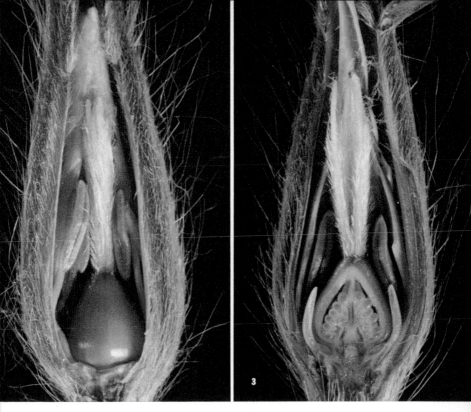

(magnified 6½ times)

The bottom row shows the development of the pistil, here stripped of its covering, at the same stages.

Pages 60 and 61 show the development of the ovules into seeds. The ovary wall has been removed (top row), and the ovary has been cut vertically (bottom row).

The top of the dry fruit splits into five teeth, each ending in a style. These curve outward, leaving an opening through which the ripe seeds will fall.

The fruit of the rose campion is a capsule.

The ovary of the rose campion flower . . .

. . . becomes a capsule which

splits at the top into five teeth.

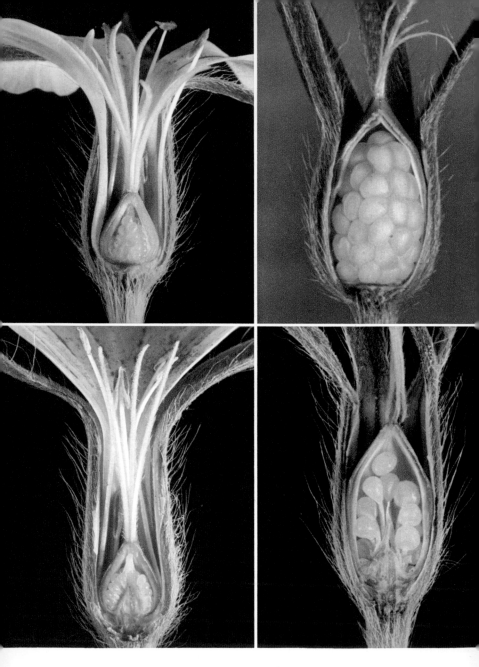

The ovules, transformed into brown

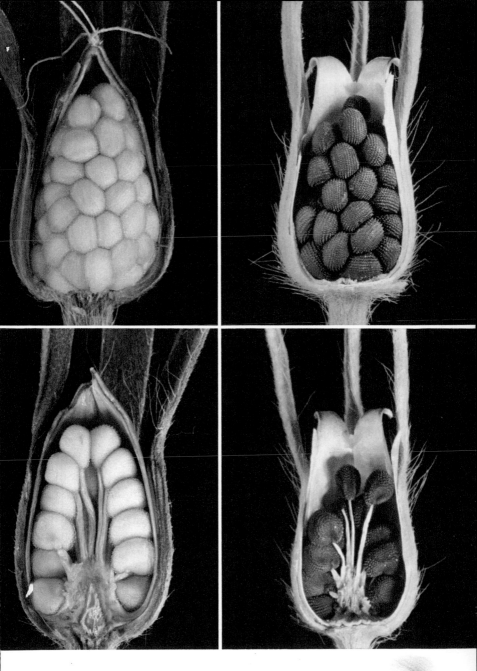

seeds, fall through the opening.

(magnified 1½ times)

The large flat fruit of the honesty developed

(slightly enlarged)

HONESTY

The big flat fruits of the honesty come from little violet flowers. Each flower contains a pistil made up of two open carpels joined at the edges; the flattened ovary contains two cells separated by the "false septum." This structure cannot be seen in the photographs.

(magnified 4 times)

from a little violet-colored flower . . .

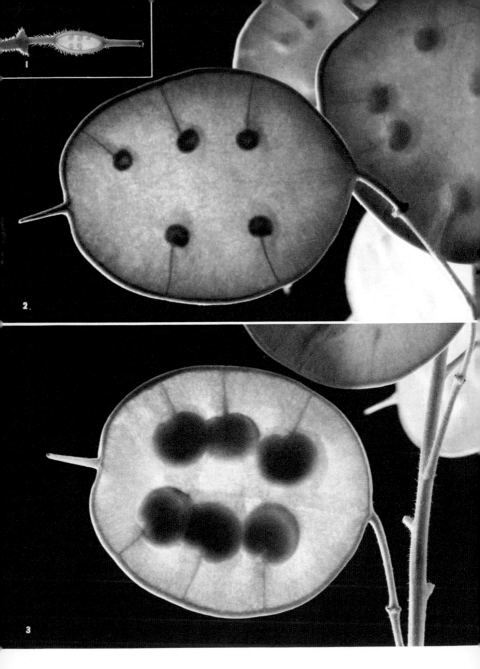

2.

3

. . . and splits open to form two valves,

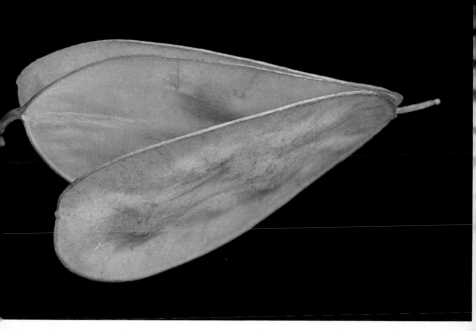

1 to 3. TRANSFORMATION OF A PISTIL INTO FRUIT
4. RIPE FRUIT OPEN

The pistil grows enormously and spreads out. The ovules, each joined by a stalk to the rim of the ovary, become large flat seeds. Their stalks grow longer.

The skin of the ripe fruit becomes dry and splits open to form two valves on either side of the central wall. The seeds then fall out. A capsule such as this is called a silique.*

---

* Some siliques do not have a central wall. Between the two valves they have only a hollow frame to which the seeds are attached.

one on each side of a central partition.

65

(magnified 11 times)

Packed with seeds, the capsule of the white

(magnified 12 times)

campion opens at the top into ten teeth.

(magnified 18½ times)

The capsule of the scarlet pimpernel

(magnified 18½ times)

opens like a box with a hinged lid.

69

(magnified 2 times)

The prickly capsule of the thorn apple

(magnified 3½ times)

splits open from top to bottom.

The capsule of the tulip opens in the

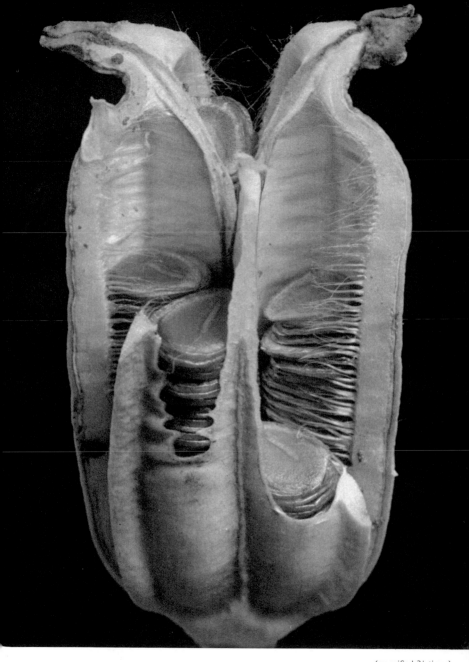

(magnified 3½ times)

same way. The seeds are neatly piled.

(slightly reduced)

The long thin capsules of the willow herb
split into four and release their
light air-borne seeds.

(magnified 7 times)

**The seeds of the snapdragon fall
through open pores at the
top of the capsules.**

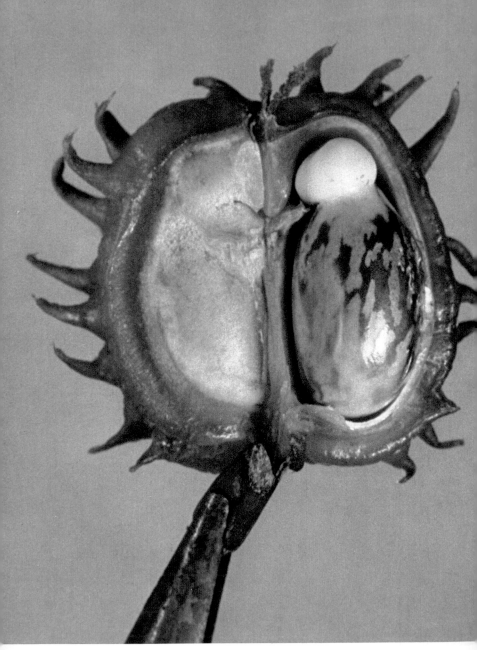

(magnified 7 times)

The capsule of the castor-oil plant

contains fat, brightly-colored seeds.

(magnified 6½ times)

The skin of this capsule splits into two thin tongues which roll up into spirals. The mustard seeds remain attached to a central frame.

Capsules of cardamine (mustard) are

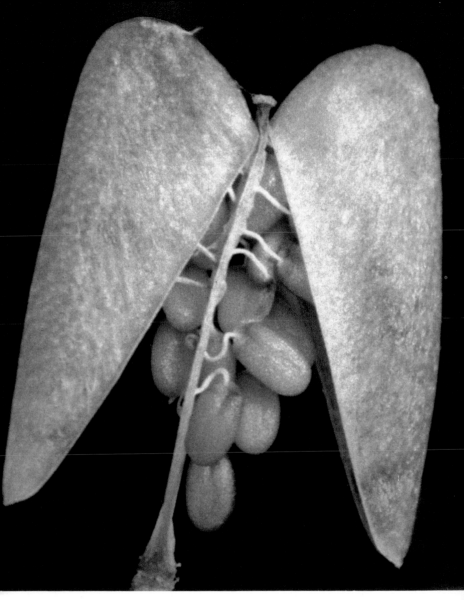

The pistils of cardamine and shepherd's-purse have the same structure as those of honesty. Their capsules are siliques.

straight; those of shepherd's-purse are large and flat.

The capsule of the pansy protects
shiny seeds.

ACHENES

An achene is a dry fruit
with a single seed and a
case which does not open.
The seed remains enclosed
in it until the time for
germination.

(magnified 6½ times)

The pasqueflower, anemone pulsatilla,

changes into a tuft of feathery fruits.

THE PASQUEFLOWER

Illus. 1. When some petals are removed we can see the many stamens arranged in several layers. The longest are in the middle and the shortest at the outside. The pistil is almost entirely hidden by this crown of stamens.

Illus. 2. When the stamens are moved, the pistil is uncovered. It consists of a large number of carpels grouped in a compact bundle. Each carpel is made up

There are many carpels.

INTERNAL VIEW OF A PASQUEFLOWER (magnified 9 times)

of an ovary supporting a long style with a stigma at its end.

Illus. 3. This picture, greatly enlarged, shows the base of the flower, cut vertically. The wall of each ovary has been removed to show the single ovule it contains. The silky appearance of the styles is due to the overlapping hairs which cover them.

Each ovary contains one ovule.

1 to 6. TRANSFORMATION OF CARPELS INTO FRUITS

Illus. 1. The flower is almost dead. The petals wither. The stamens are empty of pollen. The fertilized carpels are already beginning to swell.

Illus. 2. The bushy styles emerge from the faded flower.

The petals and stamens fade and disappear.

Illus. 3. The petals are gone. The carpels grow bigger and bigger and spread out in a large tuft. Note that one last stamen still hangs from the torus—the part of the stem that held the leaves. This gives us an idea of how much the styles have grown. The hairs of the styles are becoming disarranged.

The carpels lengthen. . .

. . . their feathery styles spread out.

Illus. 4 and 5. Slowly the carpels complete their change. The styles take on their feathery appearance.

Illus. 6. At the base of each style the ovary has become a long, thin, dry fruit. The ovule contained in it has become a seed. The ripe fruit breaks away and falls.

These dry fruits do not open; they are achenes.

The carpels, now achenes, break away from the tuft.

(slightly enlarged)
1. MAPLE TWIG IN SPRING
2. FLOWER IN BLOOM

THE MAPLE

Three flower buds have just opened, showing three sprays of flowers and a few leaves.

The maple flower is greenish and very small—only a few hundredths of an inch across. The sepals and petals are arranged around a glistening disc from which the stamens grow. The pistil in the center consists of two joined carpels. The ovary spreads sideways in two flat triangular wings. This very small pistil is going to grow enormously.

The maple blossom has a tiny pistil,

composed of two united carpels.

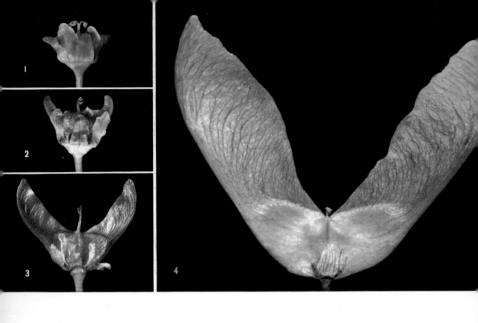

Illus. 1. The pistil has already grown greatly. The two wings of the ovary extend to left and right. We can still see the double cross formation of the stigma above the petals.

Illus. 2. The two wings become longer and longer. The stigma withers, along with the sepals and petals.

Illus. 3. The pistil keeps growing. Only a trace of the sepals and petals remains.

Illus. 4. The pistil will soon reach its maximum growth. Each carpel becomes a dry fruit with one wing. At the base of each wing is the thickened part which contains the flat seed. The ripe fruit does not open; it is an achene.

Illus. 5. The preceding photographs showed the development of a flower. This one shows two flowers that have turned into fruits; the wings of the achene are widely spread.

The pistil grows enormously;

5

each carpel becomes a winged achene.

(magnified 2 times)

There are many kinds of achenes: here are
the feathery achenes of the clematis . . .

(magnified 3 times)

the salsify achenes with their delicate parachutes . . .

(magnified 3 times)

the winged achenes of the sycamore . . .

the flat achenes of the buttercup . . .

(magnified 9 times)

**the achene of the oak—the acorn—
set in its little scaly cup,**

98

the achene of the hornbeam lodged
in a kind of three-lobed leaf . . .

(magnified 11½ times)

the strange and varied

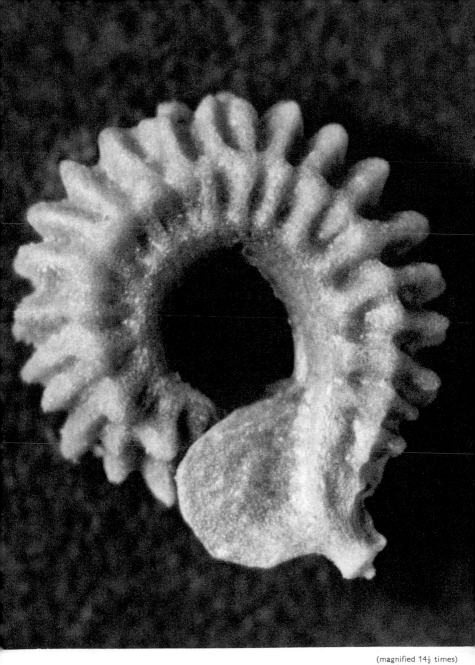

(magnified 14½ times)

achenes of the marigold . . .

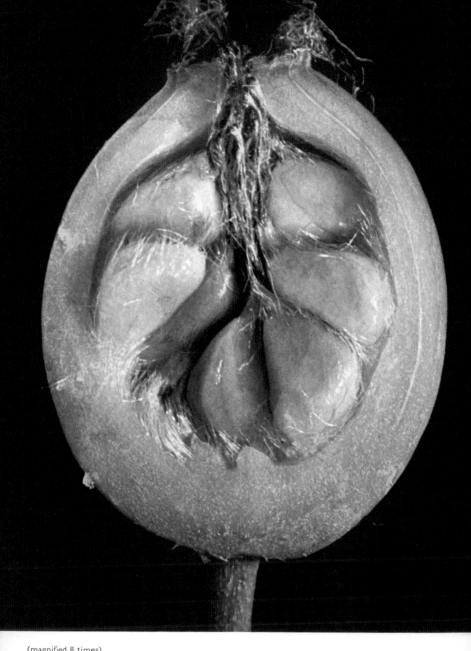

(magnified 8 times)

the hairy achenes of the wild brier;

enclosed in a little red container . . .

(magnified 8½ times)

the achenes of the scabious with their pleated

(magnified 5½ times)

collars crowned with delicately perched stars.

105

THE FRUITS WE EAT

Most of the fruits we eat are the fleshy ones. There are many edible berries too: grapes, currants, tomatoes, melons, gherkins, cucumbers, pumpkins. The date, which seems at first sight to be a drupe, is really a berry. The nut does not enclose the seed, but is itself the seed which has become hard throughout.

Oranges, tangerines and lemons are berries formed from many joined carpels. Each segment is a single carpel. The skin of the fruit—the rind—is inedible, but we eat the inside fibers which are swollen with juice and fill up the carpels' hollow interiors.

Bananas are also berries. In cultivated varieties the seeds do not develop.

The drupes—cherries, plums, apricots, peaches— provide many of our table fruits. Olives belong to this category. Walnuts and almonds are the nuts of drupes whose fleshy covering has disappeared; the seed and not the fruit is eaten. There is only one seed in the walnut; there are usually two in the almond, but often one does not develop.

The coconut is a drupe whose outer covering has become fibrous instead of fleshy. It is the stone or pit of this fruit, still covered with some of its fibers, which we see on palm trees and in the market.

Each little globule of the blackberry or the raspberry is a small drupe containing a tiny stone which, in turn, encloses the seed.

Apples and pears are halfway between berries and drupes. They contain pips (like a berry) which are surrounded by a stone (like the seeds of a drupe), but the stone is not thick and woody. It remains thin, translucent and gristly, forming five little cells in the heart of the fruit. These can be seen clearly in a cross-sectional view.

In the case of dry fruits (legumes), it is the seeds which we usually eat: the seeds from pods (kidney beans, peas, lima beans, lentils), the seeds from achenes (chestnuts, hazelnuts, beechnuts). However, some pods are used as vegetables when they are still green—for example, string(less) beans and sugar peas.

The grains of wheat, Indian corn and other cereals are dry fruits, each containing a single seed. We can consider these a special kind of achene: the outer covering of the seed and the skin of the fruit are closely joined. They cannot be separated and together form the seed container.*

The flower of the strawberry has many carpels spread over the surface of a bulging torus. It is this torus, when it has grown very large and sweet, that forms the scented flesh of the strawberry. The little dry grains scattered on its surface are the real fruits: they are achenes.

* This kind of fruit is called a caryopsis.

When the fruit is ripe a new adventure begins. The berries of the bryony and the drupes of the plum are crushed at the foot of the bush. The acorns strew the ground around the oak tree. The heavy seeds of the chestnut roll in the grass beneath the leaves. The tiny seeds of the rose campion disappear in the soil of the field. There they will germinate, send down roots, thrust up their stems, fight with their neighbors for the water, food and light which they need for growth.

Others, cast to the winds, carried by water or animals, will take their chances far from their mother plant. Perhaps they will reach a corner of the earth where competition will be less fierce and success easier. For these, the new adventure begins with a journey.

Sometimes it is the seed which travels, and sometimes the whole fruit. Some seeds have special attachments, wings or parachutes, which the wind can take hold of to help the process of scattering. The winged achene of the maple and the winged seed of the pine whirl around in the breeze which carries them along. Hanging from their parachutes, the achenes of the dandelion, salsify, coltsfoot, and thistle cover even greater distances. The still lighter downy seeds of the willow herb and poplar are carried away in clouds and glide a long way in the still air. The almost weightless seeds of the *orchis*, a kind of orchid, have no flight mechanism; the least puff of wind blows them away.

Others are carried by water: the fruits of water lilies are held up by air bubbles before sinking to the muddy bottom. Coconuts which fall on the beaches of the Pacific islands are carried away by marine currents which ultimately cast them up on some other shore.

Still others are caught and carried in the fur of animals or in the dirt sticking to the claws of birds.

Not all will find good soil where they can germinate. This does not matter, for many will succeed. Sooner or later, thanks to these traveling seeds, the volcanic island, the rubbish heap, the cracks in the old belfry will acquire their plant life; the tiniest corner of usable soil will be taken over.

Some seeds are able to germinate as soon as they leave the fruit. Most need a fairly long time to reach maturity. All need favorable conditions: warm, damp, aerated soil.

At last, when its time has come, the seed will swell with water. The little plant will burst from its covering, thrust down its root, unfold its stem and its first leaves. It will have to survive drought and frost, it will have to fight against being overgrown, and will have to escape the teeth of animals. Each day in this struggle there will be fewer survivors. But the inexhaustible fertility of life will fill the

gaps and increase the chances of each species'
continued existence and development. One day a
flower will bloom on its stalk, and the eternal cycle
will begin again.

PRINTED IN FRANCE